LE NOVELLE DELLA CIPOLLA

(Tales of the Onion)

THE ILIAD
HOMER FOR FUN

Text by Valentina Orlando
Illustrations by Celina Elmi

federighi editori

Text by
Valentina Orlando

English version by
Lesley Burgon

Illustrations and graphic project by
Celina Elmi

Executive editor
Gloria Pampaloni

Printed in December 2017 by
Federighi Colorgrafiche
Certaldo (FI)
www.federighi.com

Ist edition: June 2014
Ist reprint: December 2017

ISBN 978-88-98897-04-9
Printed in Italy

We care for the
environment by using
solar energy

The heroic happenings retold in Homer's epic poem, the *Iliad*, take us back in time to the gateway to Troy, a fortified city where a war has been waged for years between the Trojans and the Achaeans (Antique Greeks). This war was triggered not only by human action, however: the gods in the Olympus quarrel constantly and their squabbles inevitably cause havoc almost among the mortals. The gods step in to help their favourite heroes and even manage to change the course of events. Before taking a look behind the scenes of the Trojan war, let's discover which mysterious events led the Achaean army to besiege the city.

MAIN CHARACTERS
ACHAEANS (GREEKS):

Thetis: One of the Nereids, sea nymphs

Achilles: A half-god hero, son of the mortal Peleus and the sea goddess Thetis

Menelaus: King of Sparta, Helen's husband and Agamemnon's brother

Helen: Wife of Menelaus

Ulysses: King of Ithaca

Patroclus: Achilles' best friend and a soldier

Agamemnon: King of Mycenae and Menelaus' brother

TROJANS:

Priam: Hector's father and king of Troy

Paris: Priam's son and Hector's brother

Hector: Son of Priam and the Trojans' greatest hero

Hecuba: Priam's wife and Hector's mother

THE GODS:

Athena: Goddess of wisdom and of war. On the Achaean side.

Zeus: Father of all the gods. He sides with the Achaeans but also the Trojans at times.

Aphrodite: Goddess of beauty and love. On the Trojan side.

Poseidon: God of the sea. On the Achaean side.

Hera: Wife of Zeus, goddess of marriage. On the Achaean side.

Apollo: God of the sun. On the Trojan side.

It all started on Mount Olympus during the wedding banquet of Peleus, the king of Phthia, and Thetis, the most beautiful of the sea nymphs.

"You will regret not having invited me!" thundered the goddess of disharmony Eris furiously, throwing a golden apple inscribed with the words "To the fairest" in among the guests.

Consequently, the wedding party turned into a contest between the goddesses to proclaim for themselves the apple and hence the title of the most beautiful goddess of Mount Olympus.

In the end, only Hera, Athena and Aphrodite were left in the running for the title, but Zeus, unable to make up his mind, came to a decision: "It will be up to Paris, the Trojan king's son, to decide who is the most beautiful amongst you."

Paris hesitated in front of this difficult choice. Each one of the goddesses tried to gain the affections of the prince: Hera promised him eternal power, Athena promised him wisdom, and Aphrodite promised him no less than the love of the most beautiful of mortal women, Helen of Sparta. Paris put aside his doubts and chose the promise made by Aphrodite, the goddess of love.

8

Unfortunately for Paris and all the Trojans, however, Helen was already married to Menelaus, king of Sparta. So, when Paris decided to kidnap the beautiful Helen to take her with him to Troy, pandemonium was unleashed.

"I declare war on Troy!" the king of Sparta exclaimed without hesitation. Soon Agamemnon, king of Mycenae, joined his brother Menalaus in a battle cry, and soon thousands of soldiers armed with shields, armour and sharp swords joined them at the port. In the meantime, in Troy, the beautiful Helen was welcomed with joy.

9

After a long voyage, the Achaean army reached the port of Troy and the fighting began. It was the start of almost ten years of bloody battle. The Achaeans had set up camp in the large field at the base of the fortified walls of Troy. The most valued of their soldiers were Achilles, son of Thetis and Peleus, and Ulysses, the brave king of Ithaca.

Stationed on the towers, and inside the village, the Trojans defended the city and its inhabitants with all their might, commanded by Paris and his brother, the valiant Hector. But at this point, there was still no winner.

The Iliad by Homer started at the end of the ninth year of fighting in the immense valley in front of Troy.

THE FURY OF ACHILLES

Agamemnon had kidnapped the daughter of a priest of Apollo, and the furious god inflicted a terrible curse on the Greek encampment. The king had to free the maiden, but in return wanted Briseis, Achilles' slave. There was no love lost between Agamemnon and Achilles, and the conquerer couldn't forgive the insult bestowed upon him: blinded by fury, he refused to carry on fighting.

In desperation, Achilles ran onto the beach where he called upon the comfort of his mother Thetis, a sea nymph.

"I will tell Zeus everything my son, and I won't be appeased until you have your revenge!" exclaimed Thetis as she came out of the sea on the back of a dolphin. To punish Agamemnon, Zeus decided that he would favour the Trojan troops until the Achaeans asked Achilles for forgiveness. Thetis was satisfied and reassured herself over her fears of war, remembering that when Achilles was a baby she had dipped him in the waters of the river Styx as a means of making him invulnerable to weapons.

PARIS CHALLENGES MENELAUS

The land around the port of Troy trembled under the advancing Achaean army. Immediately the drawbridges of the fortress were lowered and the Trojan warriors advanced ready to fight, with Hector on the front line. Only Achilles, who was still in a rage, stayed at the port, where the Achaean ships were stationed.

One moment before the battle was due to commence, a Trojan warrior stepped forward. It was Paris.

"Throw your weapons to the floor!", he said, "I want to fight a duel with Menelaus if he is brave enough! The winner will take Helen and all the other riches!"

Menelaus promptly accepted: "I finally get the chance to take revenge for the insult I have suffered and I will win back my Helen!"

The two soldiers put on their armour and started to fight. Paris was almost beaten under the hard blows delivered by Menelaus when a blinding light shone on the battlefield.

"This way Paris, come quickly!" whispered a female voice. It was Aphrodite, who had come to his rescue. Thinking that Paris had disappeared, Menelaus brandished his sword, shouting: "Where are you, you damn coward?"

The Achaeans searched long and hard, but Paris was nowhere to be found. Aphrodite had spirited him away safe and sound to his bedchamber.

On the battlefield, Agamemnon spoke: "Seeing as Paris has disappeared without a trace, I declare Menelaus the winner. However, give us back Helen and all the promised riches, and the Achaeans will be acknowledged as the winners of the Trojan war!"

It appeared as if the war had reached its conclusion, but on the top of mount Olympus, a huge argument about the outcome of the battles was unleashed. In the end Zeus was forced to intervene, and sent Athena to join the armies. The goddess made a Trojan warrior wound

Menelaus with an arrow and the Achaeans, believing that they were being betrayed declared in fury: "Let the battle resume!"

Thus bloody battles and moments of truce followed.

The Trojans, led by Hector, fought off the Achaean assaults on more than one occasion, and frequently succeeded in attacking the enemy camp, so much so that Agamemnon and his troops hurried to build a high wall to defend their ships.

As anxiety wound its way amongst the Achaean soldiers, the army chiefs decided to go and speak to Agamemnon: "We can't think about conquering Troy while Achilles stays in the background. He must come back and fight. He's our most valiant soldier!"

So Agamemnon decided to make up with Achilles and sent Ulysses and some other ambassadors to him laden with luxurious gifts.

"The Achaean army needs you," explained Ulysses, "put your pride to one side and take up your weapons again. Sitting here in your tent isn't the way to receive your glory!" Achilles hesitated; to see his army suffer made him unhappy and touched him deeply, but he replied to Ulysses by saying "I'm sorry, but I cannot forget the insult I have received." And with that, Achilles refused Agamemnon's gifts and sent the ambassadors away. The situation became steadily worse for the Greeks. Hector was ruthless and had by now led the Trojan army towards the port.

"Attack the defense wall and set fire to the Greek ships!" he ordered.

The Achaeans seemed doomed. As the flames advanced towards the ships, Poseidon, the god of the sea, emerged from the water in a vortex of sea spray to intervene on behalf of the Greeks. Therefore with this divine protection, the Achaeans saved themselves from the attacks.

ZEUS' PLAN

Zeus, making use of his well-known astuteness, put into place a plan to make Achilles return to battle. On the Achaean battle line was a dear friend of Achilles, Patroclus, whom he had known from childhood. One day he visited Achilles with a proposal.

"My dear friend," he begged, kneeling on the floor in front of him, "if you really don't want to rejoin the battle, at least lend me your armour and your immortal horses and allow me, pretending to be you, to fight in your place."

Achilles completely trusted his friend and knowing that the fiery arrows of Hector were getting closer and closer to the Greek fleet of ships, he accepted the proposal. "Very well," he said, "we must stop our ships from being set alight or we'll never be able to return home, but promise me you will only scare him and then back off as soon as the enemy starts to withdraw! At that point I will be ready to personally intervene to inflict the final blow on the Trojans and finally take hold of the city!"

"I am grateful to you," replied Patroclus, "the

Trojans will believe they are confronted with you, the great Achilles and they will be afraid."
After shaking his friend's hand, he rushed to the battlefield.

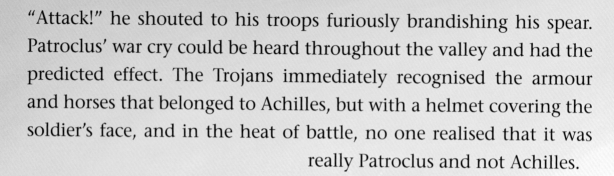

"Attack!" he shouted to his troops furiously brandishing his spear. Patroclus' war cry could be heard throughout the valley and had the predicted effect. The Trojans immediately recognised the armour and horses that belonged to Achilles, but with a helmet covering the soldier's face, and in the heat of battle, no one realised that it was really Patroclus and not Achilles.

"Taste the Achaean swords!" shouted Patroclus as he massacred Trojan after Trojan. Zeus made sure that the winning spirit was kept strong in the soldier, so much so that when Hector killed one of Patroclus' dearest friends in battle, the soldier's fury became even harsher. Forgetting Achilles' instructions, Patroclus drove straight on up to the Trojan gates. At sunset the battlefield was awash with dead bodies.

With the Achaean army in advantage, the god Apollo decided to intervene in Troy's defence and struck Patroclus in the back so hard that the bronze helmet he was wearing fell to the floor and split in two. Hector immediately went up to Patroclus: "Did you think that you could enter Troy, ransack our houses and kidnap our women? You are just fooling yourself! You will die here and now, beneath these walls! Where is your dear friend Achilles now? He is keeping his bravery for himself!"

He raised his spear to the sky and with one blow, ran it through Patroclus' body. Then Hector put on the dead man's armour and took his sword, which really belonged to Achilles, and turned to the Achaeans threateningly: "I will drag his dead body inside these walls and feed it to the dogs!"

Menelaus, who had witnessed the whole

thing, rushed to defend the honour of his dead Achaean companion and new fighting broke out around the lifeless body of Patroclus.

In the meantime, a messenger had been sent to inform Achilles, who was still at the port, far away from the battlefield, of the bad news: "Patroclus is dead and has been robbed of his shield and armour by Hector."

On hearing these words, Achilles plunged into despair and shouted in anger: "I want revenge now! I have been too long out of battle and the moment has come to take my sword in my hand again!"

Zeus' plan had worked to perfection: sacrificing Patroclus meant that Achilles wanted to fight once more.

Heroic Achilles raced to the battlefield and let out an almighty cry. The enemies were afraid and decided to withdraw towards Troy. It meant that the Achaeans had a reprieve and were able to recover Patroclus' body and bring it back to the camp.

ACHILLES' REVENGE

Night fell and Thetis asked Hephaestus, the Greek god of blacksmiths, to forge some sharp and shiny new weapons and at sunrise, she handed them to her son. An oracle had predicted that the Trojan war would be won when Achilles stepped in, and so when the news that the great hero would be returning to fight reached the Greek camp, everyone jumped for joy.

"Today will see the end of my fury towards Agamemnon," said Achilles, during a meeting amongst the army leaders, "Hector and the Trojans have taken advantage of our disagreements for too long. It's time to look towards the future and win this war!"

Agamemnon, injured with war wounds, wanted to offer precious gifts to Achilles as a sign of peace, but the hero was engrossed in thought about the imminent battle and ignored them.

"Quick! Prepare the horses it's time to take action!" he said to the jubilant crowd. Achilles was furious and looked for Hector amongst the soldiers, bent on revenge. Apollo however intervened, protecting the Trojan leader.

All the enemies that happened to be in Achilles path were killed mercilessly.

Priam, the old king, posted up in the tower, saw Achilles approach Troy and raised the alarm: "Get back! Open the drawbridge and let all our soldiers get to safety inside the walls."

Once they were safely inside, they wiped the sweat from their brow and had something to eat, aided by the Trojan women. Priam and Hecuba begged their son Hector to retreat inside the walls.

"I am not a coward. I will go back to Troy a winner, once I've killed Achilles, otherwise, if it is my destiny, I'll die gloriously on the battlefield."

Left alone outside the walls of Troy, Hector started to provoke a reaction from the enemy and said: "Come out cowardly

Achilles! Where are you hiding?
I'll fight you until the last breath."
And that's how things proceeded.

THE DEATH OF HECTOR

Achilles missed the first strike, with the spear landing nearby.
"You missed just like a beginner!" mocked Hector.
The goddess Athena in the meantime, without being seen by Hector,
quickly picked up the spear and gave it back to Achilles.
When Hector struck back at Achilles, his spear bounced off Achilles'
shield, that had been given to him by his mother.

Disarmed, Hector waited in vain for a divine intervention, a helping hand, or a new weapon, but when nothing came to him, he soon realised that he had been abandoned by the gods. Achilles took advantage of this. He placed his shield in front of his chest and started advancing towards the enemy. His spear glistened like a star in the night sky. Achilles aimed at a part of Hector that wasn't protected by the armour he had stolen from Patroclus and hurled the spear at his bare neck.

The spear stuck him and the last words that the Trojan hero spoke were: "For pity's sake Achilles, show you have a heart and give my body back to my father Priam so that the Trojan population can pay me their respects."

Achilles replied that he would not grant his last wish for all the money in the world and that his body would be subject to a brutal treatment. Under the horrified eyes of the Trojan population that had gathered along the fortress walls and on the ramparts, Achilles tied Hectors body onto his wagon by his ankles and let loose the horses, who pulled him round through the dust like a sort of gruesome trophy.

THE FUNERAL OF PATROCLUS

Feeling satisfied that he had avenged Patroclus' death, Achilles held a banquet along the shore for the Achaeans. It lasted until late into the night when he finally fell asleep, with only the sound of the waves filling the air.

That night as he slept, Patroclus' spirit visited him in a dream to say one final goodbye so he asked him to organize his funeral.

At the break of dawn, everything was prepared for the last farewell to Patroclus. Following an ancient tradition, Achilles decided to organize some games in his friend's honour, starting with chariot race and followed by a boxing match, an archery contest and discus throw.

Once these gloomy games had finished, the ashes of Patroclus were placed in a golden urn around which Achilles had a sepulchre built.

HECTOR RETURNS TO TROY

The fury of Achilles after the death of Hector wasn't easily placated and consequently, Hector's body was left lying in the dust.

Seeing Achilles behaviour, some of the gods got angry and on Mount Olympus they were soon arguing once more on what should be done. Zeus was forced to step in for the umpteenth time and sent a divine messenger to Priam, who suggested: "Go to Achilles with some gifts in exchange for your son's body."

"Don't go Priam," implored his wife Hecuba, "it is most certainly a trap to kill you." But the distressed king decided to accept the advice of the gods.

As soon as night had fallen, he filled a chariot with precious cloaks, carpets, splendid amphorae and other gems and went to Achilles. The Greek hero had just finished dinner and was alone.

Once inside his tent, Priam implored Achilles to give him back his son's body and to accept in exchange the rich gifts that he had brought with him. Achilles was so surprised by the visit from the king of Troy himself and his words, that he found himself remembering his own, distant father. Moved by this, he shook the king's hand and accepted the exchange.

"What a strange destiny! Trojans and Achaeans have lost a lot of their heroes but there still is no winner," he added, letting Priam leave with his son's body.

Together with Hector's body, Priam also took with him a promise from Achilles, who said: "There will be no further attack on our

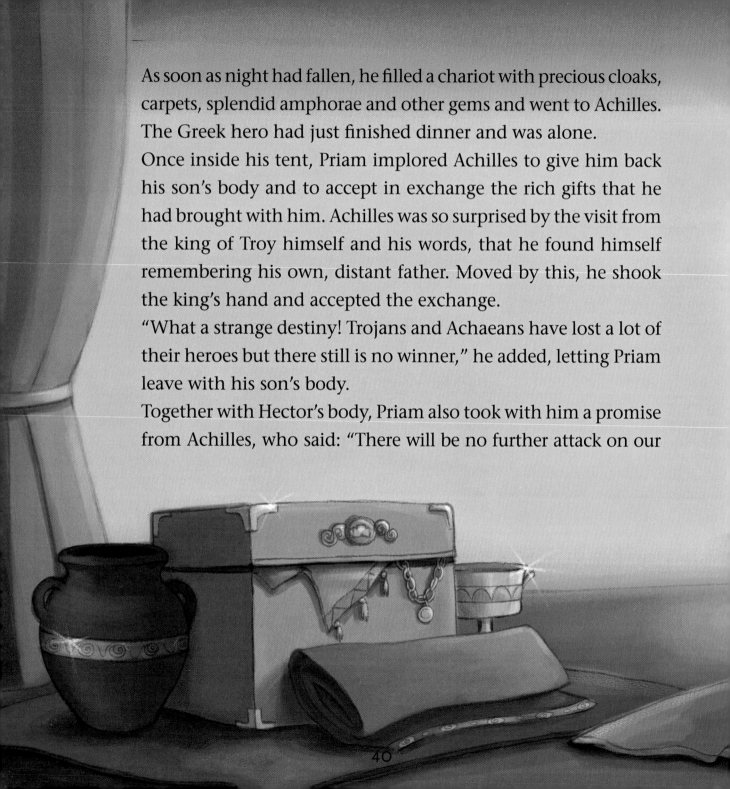

part for at least twelve days, the time necessary to organize the funeral of your prince." After being mourned by his people, Hector's soul could finally rest in peace.

THE END OF THE WAR

That's how the story of the *Iliad* by Homer ends.
But how did the Trojan war finish? And what happened to all the heroes in this book? Let's find out:

Hector, the Trojan leader was dead, but Troy was still intact.
The Greeks were only able to penetrate the fortified city thanks to an astute plan that went down in history as the story of the Trojan Horse. This story is dealt with in another famous poem by Homer, the

Odyssey, that tells of the return of Ulysses to Ithaca after the war. This brilliant idea came from Ulysses himself, who had an enormous wooden horse built, so big that numerous Greek soldiers could hide inside it. They then drove it to the port of Troy.

44

The Trojans, seeing the Greek camp half empty, thought that they had fled, and noticing the horse, believed that it was a gift to honour the gods. Thus, they decided to pull it inside the city walls.

Ulysses and his men waited until the dead of night and then came out and killed many Trojans as they slept. The Trojans fought with great courage, but the Greeks had the upper hand.

In the end, Troy was conquered by the Achaeans, ransacked and looted, and its people were either killed or reduced to slavery. The loot was then divided up between the survivors and when there was nothing left, the Achaeans went back to their ships and set sail towards home after years of absence.

The great hero Achilles was killed by Paris, who hit him in the heel with an arrow. When he was just an infant, his mother, Thetis, had dipped him in the sacred river to make him immortal, and had held him by the heel, which had thus remained the only vulnerable part of his body. The beautiful Helen returned to Menelaus from Sparta while on the horizon Troy by now looked like a long expanse of blazing ruins.

For some, such as Ulysses, the journey home was long and arduous…

Book series by
FEDERIGHI EDITORI:

LE NOVELLE DELLA CIPOLLA
(Tales of the Onion)

Boccaccio for Fun
Brother Cipolla - Chichibìo - Calandrino and the heliotrope

The Decameron by Giovanni Boccaccio
Calandrino and the stolen pig - Costanza and Martuccio

Dante for Fun - Hell

Dante for Fun - Purgatory

Dante for Fun - Paradise

Manzoni for Fun - The Betrothed

Homer for Fun - The Odyssey

Shakespeare for Fun - Romeo and Juliet

Ovid for Fun vol.1
The Labyrinth of the Minotaur - Daedalus and Icarus

SCIENZE ED ARTI NEL RINASCIMENTO
(Sciences and Arts in the Renaissance)

Playing with Leonardo - The Vitruvian Man

Playing with Leonardo - The Divine Proportion

Playing with Piero della Francesca - Geometry at the Service of the Arts

I GRANDI PER GIOCO
(Great Personalities for Fun)

My Secret Adventure with Leonardo

Dante Alighieri - His own story

They called me Caravaggio

LE NOVELLE DELLA CIPOLLA *JUNIOR*
(Tales of the Onion junior)

Play with Pinocchio

OTHER BOOKS
Play with Leonardo da Vinci